SONIC™
THE HEDGEHOG
30th ANNIVERSARY

CELEBRATION

IDW

Nachie Marsham, Publisher
Blake Kobashigawa, SVP Sales, Marketing & Strategy
Tara McCrillis, VP Publishing Operations
Anna Morrow, VP Marketing & Publicity
Alexandra Hargett, VP Sales

Cover Art by
Yui Karasuno of Sonic Team

Scott Dunbier, Director, Special Projects

Series Assistant Edits by
Riley Farmer

Lauren LePera, Managing Editor
Joe Hughes, Director, Talent Relations
Keith Davidsen, Director, Marketing & PR
Topher Alford, Sr. Digital Marketing Manager

Series Edits by
David Mariotte

Patrick O'Connell, Sr. Manager, Direct Market Sales
Shauna Monteforte, Sr. Director of Manufacturing Operations
Greg Foreman, Director DTC Sales & Operations

Collection Edits by
Alonzo Simon
and Zac Boone

Nathan Widick, Sr. Art Director, Head of Design
Neil Uyetake, Sr. Art Director, Design & Production
Shawn Lee, Art Director, Design & Production

Collection Design
& Lettering by
Shawn Lee

Jack Rivera, Art Director, Marketing

Ted Adams and Robbie Robbins, IDW Founders

ISBN: 978-1-68405-926-3
25 24 23 22   2 3 4 5

Facebook: facebook.com/idwpublishing
Twitter: @idwpublishing
YouTube: youtube.com/idwpublishing
Instagram: @idwpublishing

My first encounter with Sonic occurred very young within a '90s video rental store, not on the screen but eyeing a simple poster. Wagging his finger at me with his trademark 'tude and casually crossed shoes, his electric-blue presence instantly connected with me; "Who is that blue cat?!" (Sonic is a Hedgehog). At this point in time I had no idea what videogames were, but his silhouette and expression were strong enough that *Sonic 2* was the immediate pick when my school friend invited me over to play on his Sega console.

The first moments were intoxicating. Here was a character who rocketed through vibrant geometric worlds like a living embodiment of a skateboard, rolling and ricocheting off robotic enemies and other Rube Goldberg contraptions in a way that felt gravity defying. Sonic doesn't need wheels to go fast, because he himself is the wheel, reinvented! Opposing him is Dr. Eggman (aka Dr. Robotnik), who, while being a malicious mad scientist bent on world domination, clearly is also a child at heart, with modular vehicles that would be the envy of any meccano enthusiast. And perhaps crucially for me, beating the game was only the beginning; the real way to play *Sonic* was to turn on the debug mode cheat and spend hours causing untold havoc within the game! This is rather fitting given Sonic's own rebellious devil-may-care attitude, and served as my first glimpse behind the smoke and mirrors (or sprites and tiles) of game development...

So, unless you've been living in Hidden Palace Zone, you're probably keenly aware that 2021 is the 30th anniversary of our favorite blue fella. Sonic's world has evolved significantly since the heyday of the '90s and means different things to people depending on who you ask. As someone who both grew up with and has been able to contribute to the series as lead developer on *Sonic Mania*, the signature style and sensibilities of the classic 16-Bit era of Sonic is a world woven from a tapestry of many pop-culture influences from the 20th Century. From pinball and parlor games, to Art Deco and Memphis Milano, to New Jack Swing and the Manchester music scene, it is a world that I feel is still rich for exploration in the here and now.

Okay, okay! You want to know what's so special about this collection, right? This is IDW's first foray into the world of Classic Sonic and…

It's got lots of colorful Classic Zones old and new!

It's got lots of characters! (even some deep cuts for you super fans)

It's the first Hard Boiled Heavies comic debut! (I'm so proud of those eggheads)

If you are learning to draw your favorite characters in the classic style, this collection has got so many legit poses! (shout-out to SATAM Robotnik confusing me very much as a kid)

Sonic is 30 now, so let's not keep him waiting any longer. His next adventure begins with but a turn of the page!

Christian Whitehead
Creative Director @ Evening Star

YOW!

NO WORRIES. I'LL JUST REACH OUT AND GRAB A PERFECTLY TIMED AIR-SUPPORT RESCUE FROM MY BESTEST BUDDY IN THE WHOLE WORLD...

--KNUCKLES?!

SONIC.

WHAT ARE YOU DOING SO FAR FROM HOME?

THERE'S TROUBLE. YOU SEE...

HIS TRAIL LED ME HERE. I SAW THE BUSINESS WITH METAL SONIC, AND YOU KNOW THE REST.

WOW! METAL SONIC *AND* METAL KNUCKLES!

DR. EGGMAN MUST HAVE SENT THEM! IF HE'S AFTER THE CHAOS EMERALDS, THEN HE'S UP TO SOMETHING! WE HAVE TO STOP HIM!

THAT'S THE SPIRIT, KID!

AND WE'RE JUST THE HEROES TO GET THE JOB DONE!

EEEEEE! ANOTHER EXCITING ADVENTURE WITH SONIC!

AND *THIS* TIME, I'M AROUND AT THE VERY START!

I GET TO SEE ALL THE ACTION! I GET TO--

--OH.

BOING

HA!

HEY! WHAT ARE YOU DOING BACK THERE, DOUBLE-BUTT?

THROWING OFF YOUR CALIBRATIONS.

WHA--?

SONIC! I GOT THE EMERALD!

--CRASH

BOIN--

24

25

27

WITH THAT, ALL THE CHAOS EMERALDS ARE ACCOUNTED FOR.

TWO HAVE BEEN DELIVERED.

THE THIRD IS HELD BY THE AMATEURS.

METAL KNUCKLES IS BRINGING THE FOURTH.

THE BUFFOONS ARE CLOSING IN ON THE FIFTH.

METAL SONIC HAS ACQUIRED THE SIXTH AND MOVES TO ACQUIRE THE SEVENTH AND FINAL GEM...

34

"...IT ALL STARTED WHEN I DECIDED TO REBUILD HEAVY KING, YOU SEE.

"HE WOULD BECOME MY CHIEF COMMANDER AND LEAD MY ROBOTS INTO BATTLE.

"THAT WAY, I'D HAVE MORE TIME TO INVENT, RESEARCH... YOU KNOW, DO IMPORTANT STUFF.

"EVERYTHING WAS GOING GREAT..."

YOUR SYMPATHY IS OVERWHELMING.

GET ON WITH IT. WHAT'S HEAVY KING UP TO WITH THE CHAOS EMERALDS?

WHAT DO YOU THINK, DOLT? ONCE HE HAS THE ULTIMATE POWER, HE'LL BE UNSTOPPABLE!

I HIRED THEM TO GATHER THE GEMS FIRST, BUT CLEARLY YOU MESSED THINGS UP LIKE YOU ALWAYS DO!

HOW WERE YOU PLANNING ON REWARDING US IF YOU'RE ON YOUR OWN?

O-ONCE I'M BACK IN COMMAND, YOU'LL BE RICHLY COMPENSATED! P-PROMISE!

UH-HUH.

LOOKS LIKE WE'RE WORKIN' TOGETHER FOR NOW, FLEET-FEET.

SURE. IF YOU CAN KEEP UP!

WINTER CAVERNS ZONE.

ACCORDING TO THE RADAR, ALL THE CHAOS EMERALDS ARE IN THE BASE UP AHEAD.

WELL, THAT'S NO GOOD.

BETTER GET IN THERE QUICK BEFORE HE USES THEM!

BUT WE'RE TOUGHER!

GAH! WHAT ARE YOU DOING?! GET OUT THERE AND FIGHT!

IF HEAVY KING IS CONTROLLING THEM REMOTELY, MAYBE WE CAN STOP HIS SIGNAL FROM HERE?

OF COURSE! THAT'S WHAT I WAS TRYING TO DO WITH METAL SONIC! A JAMMING SIGNAL AT THIS RANGE WILL REVERT THEM TO THEIR BASE PROGRAMMING, AND THEY'LL OBEY ME AGAIN! I'M A GENIUS!

YAAAAH!

ALRIGHT! THEY DON'T WORK FOR HEAVY KING ANYMORE!

OH, NO! THEY'RE WORKING FOR DR. EGGMAN AGAIN!

KNOCK IT OFF, YOU TWO! THEY'RE WORKING WITH ME... FOR NOW!

THAT'S RIGHT! WE'RE ALL ON THE SAME TEAM! DON'CHA JUST LOVE THAT?

WELP, NOW THAT THAT'S SETTLED, TIME TO KNOCK ON THE DOOR.

AND BY "KNOCK," I MEAN "LIBERAL USE OF HIGH EXPLOSIVES."

NOPE. I AIN'T HAVING YOU CAVING IN THE WHOLE PLACE.

WHERE'S YOUR SENSE OF EXCITEMENT?! YOUR ARTISTIC VISION?!

LOOKS PRETTY STURDY, EVEN FOR ME. SO WHAT DO YOU SAY--ON THREE?

ONE!

TWO!

THR--!

NO, NO, STOP! I JUST HAD THEM PAINTED!

I'LL OPEN THEM MYSELF!

SO...
BEAUTIFUL...!

WHAT?

AH. HIS PLAN. I FELL FOR IT.

AND NOW YOU'LL FALL FOR THIS!

VREE-VREE-VREE

BRAK

CONSIDER YOURSELF USURPED.

I YIELD AND BEG MERCY.

DID YOU NOT PROGRAM ME TO BE DECEITFUL AND CONQUEST-DRIVEN?

HAVE I NOT BEEN FULFILLING MY FUNCTION?

YOU'RE *TECHNICALLY* RIGHT.

THE BEST KIND OF RIGHT.

AND YOU WERE EFFECTIVE UP UNTIL YOUR BETRAYAL...

WHERE IS EVERYONE?

APOLOGIES, SIR. THEY MUST HAVE LEFT WHILE YOU WERE THREATENING ME.

WELL THEN MARSHAL MY FORCES AND TRACK THEM DOWN! THEY CAN'T HAVE GOTTEN FAR!

APOLOGIES, SIR. YOU HAD THEM DESTROY ALL THE BADNIKS WHILE INVADING MY BASE. YOUR BASE.

METAL SONIC! METAL KNUCKLES! CHASE THEM DOWN AND--EH?!

APOLOGIES, SIR. AFTER EMERALD-HUNTING NON-STOP, FIGHTING EVERYONE AND MY EMPOWERED SELF, THEY'VE RUN OUT OF ENERGY.

THIS HAS BEEN AN AWFUL DAY. MAKE ME A GRILLED CHEESE.

APOLO-GIES, SIR. I AM HEAVY KING. NOT HEAVY CHEF.

THE SPEED LIMIT! IT DICTATES HOW FAST YOU'RE ALLOWED TO DRIVE IN A GIVEN AREA!

OH! WHAT WILL THEY THINK OF NEXT?

GUESS I'LL... STOP... HITTING THE GAS SO MUCH?

AND THE CAR WILL EVENTUALLY... NOT BE FAST, ANYMORE?!

SORRY, KIP. WE'RE IN UNCHARTED WATERS HERE.

THE BRAKES, SONIC.

THE BRAKES MAKE THE CAR STOP.

OH, WOW! OKAY! I THOUGHT THAT WAS THE TURBO PEDAL OR SOMETHING!

THERE'S... THERE'S NO TURBO PEDAL, SONIC.

WE'RE IN A NORMAL CAR.

MY NORMAL CAR.

RIGHT, YEAH! NO, I GET IT NOW, TOTALLY.

HERE WE GO.

TIME TO SLOW THINGS RIGHT ON DOWN.

YES. PLEASE.

YOU'RE... GOING TO HAVE TO PRESS HARDER THAN THAT.

HERE'S THE WEIRD THING, KIP, I'M TRYING TO. I SWEAR.

SHOULD TOUCHING IT MAKE ME SICK?

"HERE'S YOUR TRAFFIC UPDATE, BROUGHT TO YOU BY TOON'S FESTOONS, FOR THE BEST IN FESTOONERY--"

MR. SONIC, IF YOU DON'T MIND MY ASKING--

QUILLSBROOK ROAD

--WHAT ARE YOU DOING HERE?

LEARNING TO DRIVE, OF COURSE!

WITH MY NEW FRIEND AND MENTOR, KIP THE CAPYBARA!

THE BEST DRIVING INSTRUCTOR IN THE BIZ!

≥SIGH≤

RED LIGHT, SONIC! OTHER CARS ARE IN THE INTERSECTION!

OH SHOOT, YOU'RE RIGHT! I'M ON IT!

"THERE SEEMS TO BE SOME PROBLEMS IN THE QUILLSBROOK ROAD AREA.

"WE'LL KEEP AN EYE ON IT."

WHY ARE YOU LEARNING TO DRIVE, SONIC? WHAT DO YOU NEED A CAR FOR?

OH! RIGHT, THAT'S EASY.

TWO WORDS, KIP, ONE OF WHICH IS REALLY LONG AND DRAWN OUT, FOR EMPHASIS.

CHILI DAWWWGSSSS.

YOU NEED A CAR... FOR HOT DOGS?

CHILI DOGS, KIP. HOT DOGS WITH CHILI.

BUT... WHY--

LONG GONE ARE THE DAYS WHERE YOU'RE FORCED TO CHOOSE BETWEEN HOT DOGS AND CHILI FOR DINNER, KIP!

THE HOT DOG SCIENTISTS HAVE PUT THE CHILI RIGHT SMACK DAB ON THERE.

HAVE YOU EVER HEARD OF... MR. MUNCH-UM'S BUN-SIZED FRANKS?

THEY'RE THE BEST CHILI DOGS ON THE PLANET!

THEY GET THE CHILI TO DOG RATIO SO RIGHT!

ANYWAYS, MR. MUNCH-UM'S IS HOSTING A RALLY RACE.

BUT, GET THIS--IT'S A CAR RACE.

I THINK I FOLLOW.

SO, I'M GUESSING THE GRAND PRIZE IS--

--CHILI DAWGSSS.

GOOD! OKAY, NOW WE'RE GETTING SOMEWHERE.

SPEED LIMIT 50

SCHOOL ZONE'S COMING UP. LET'S MAKE USE OF THOSE BRAKES, HUH?

URGH. IT GOES SLOWER?!

ON YOUR LEFT!

DON'T FORGET YOUR TURN SIGNAL!

RIGHT... THEY CAN'T JUST HEAR ME YELL...

REMEMBER, TWO CAR'S LENGTH FROM THE CAR IN FRONT!

WE'RE SHARING THE ROAD, RIGHT?

MUCH BETTER! MUCH, MUCH BETTER!

YEAH. RIGHT. BETTER. LEARNING TO DRIVE IS FUN. WHEE.

SPC 1292

"AND DON'T FORGET, COMING UP IN FIVE MINUTES, WE'LL GO TO OUR LIVE COVERAGE OF THE MR. MUNCHEM'S ROAD RALLY--"

KTBR199.2

WHAATTT?!

FIVE MINUTES?! IT'S NOT SUPPOSED TO BE UNTIL THE 12TH!

TODAY IS THE 12TH.

OKAY, I GUESS WE CAN WRAP THIS--

--UUUUPPPP!

I KNOW A SHORTCUT. IF WE WANT TO GET THERE ON TIME, GONNA HAVE TO TAKE... THE LOOP!

NONONONONO!

THIS CAR CAN'T DO THE LOOP!

NO NEED TO WORRY ABOUT THAT, KIPSTER--

--THIS DRIVER HAS DONE IT, LIKE, A JILLION TIMES!

DR. EGGMAN'S BIRTHDAY

BAH!

LOOK OUT WHEN THE STORM'S THROUGH... EGGMAN WILL PULVERIZE YOU...

IT'S MY BIRTHDAY AGAIN, ISN'T IT.

"EVERY YEAR, I'M PULLED AWAY FROM MY WORK BY THIS NONSENSE."

"I'VE TOLD THE FOOLS TIME AND TIME AGAIN TO KNOCK IT OFF..."

"...BUT THAT ONLY SEEMS TO HAVE ENCOURAGED THEM."

WELL, THEN, LET'S GET IT OVER WITH.

I'M ON TO YOU!

COME OUT--

--AND--

--GET BACK TO WORK!

THEY CAN'T BE SERIOUS.

WOW, AMY, YOU DIDN'T HAVE TO DO ALL THIS.

IT WAS MY PLEASURE!

WHAT'S SONIC UP TO THIS TIME?

JUST PATROLLING AROUND. I THINK HE GETS A LITTLE STIR-CRAZY IF HE STANDS STILL FOR, OH, TWO SECONDS.

I BET THAT'S CAUSED A FEW PROBLEMS.

A FEW!

ONE TIME, WE WERE OUT LOOKING FOR EGGMAN'S NEW SECRET BASE, RIGHT?

WE DECIDED TO HIDE OUT, WAIT FOR A GROUP OF BADNIKS TO SHOW UP, AND SEE WHERE THEY WENT.

WHICH MEANS STAYING QUIET AND STAYING STILL.

BUT, OF COURSE, THE MOMENT SONIC SAW THE BADDIES, HE BLASTED OUT OF THE BUSHES AND--

MM-HMM.

--SPIN-DASHED ALL OF THEM?

HEY, WHAT ARE YOU DOING?

ACK!

TAKING NOTES ON SONIC?

YOU AREN'T SECRETLY WORKING FOR EGGMAN OR SOMETHING, ARE YOU?

WHAT? NO!

I JUST--

--PROMISE YOU WON'T MAKE FUN OF ME?

Amy Rose

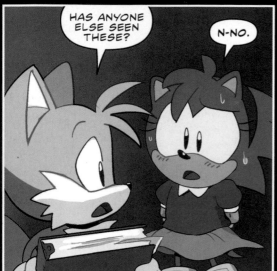

HAS ANYONE ELSE SEEN THESE?

N-NO.

THEY AREN'T VERY GOOD.

HOLD ON A SEC.

HEY!

COMING THROUGH, COMING THROUGH...!

...WHAT'S GOING ON?

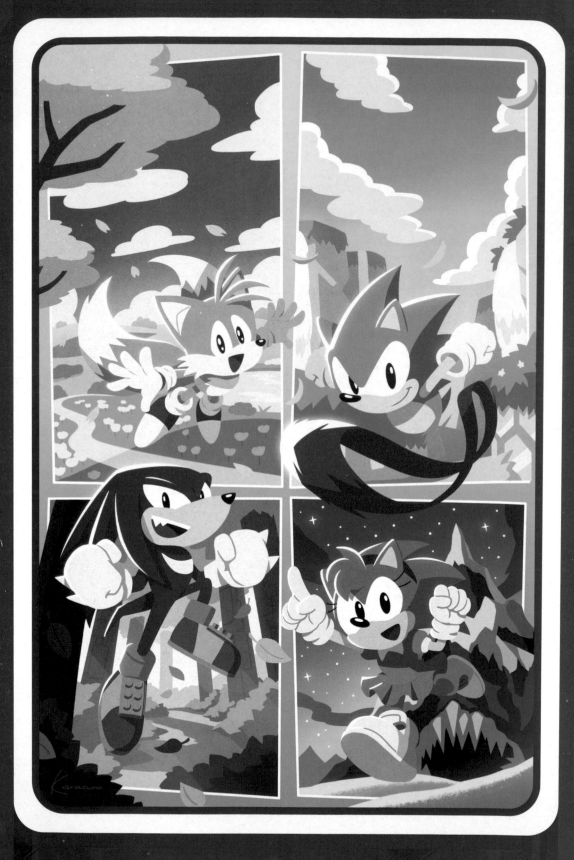

ART **YUI KARASUNO** FOR SONIC TEAM

CHRISTINA-ANTOINETTE NEOFOTISTOU

PATRICK SPAZIANTE

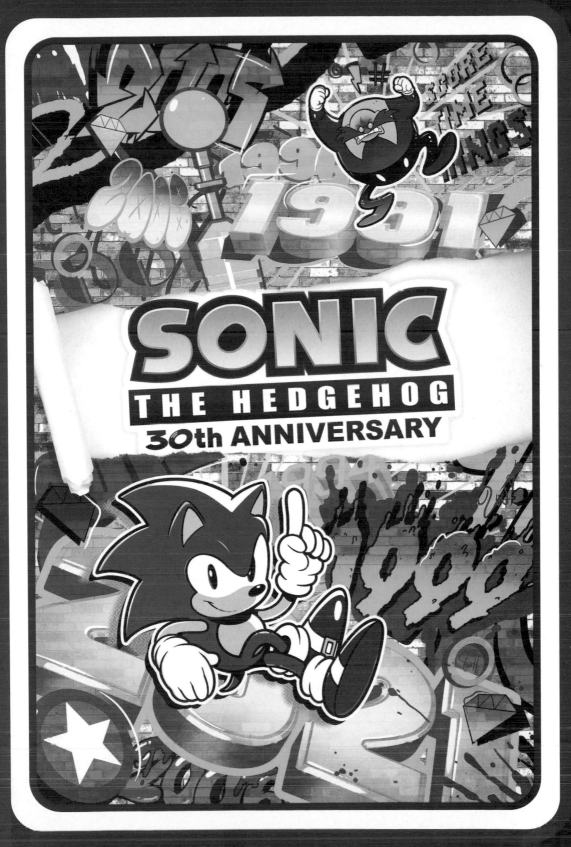

SONIC
THE HEDGEHOG
30th ANNIVERSARY

TYSON HESSE

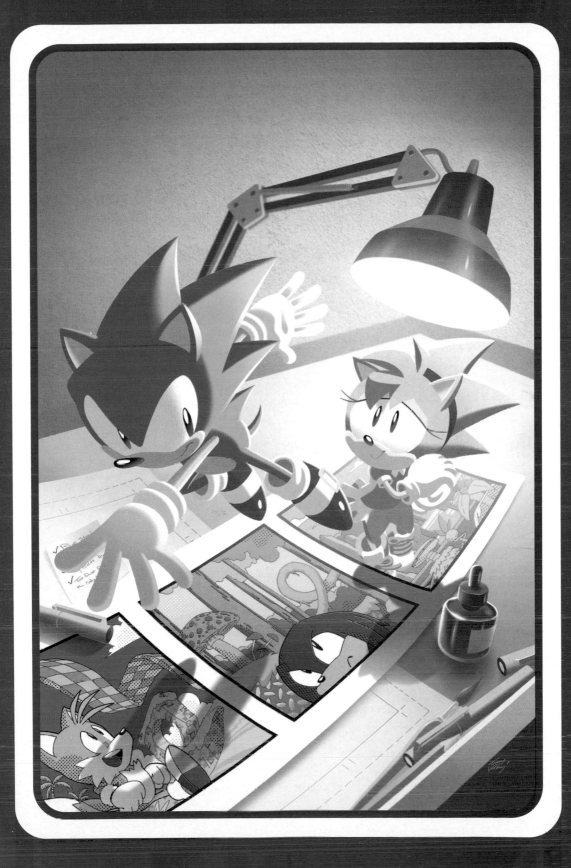

TRACY YARDLEY

FROM SCRIPT TO PAGE

Have you ever wondered how comics are made? Like in the story "Amy's New Hobby," they take a lot of hard work, thought, and often a little bit of help from your friends! Join us on a tour of the comic making process that brought you this collection as we go behind the scenes of how comics are made!

Just like Sonic assembled his friends (and foes) in "Seasons of Chaos," the first step to making a comic is putting together a creative team. Many comics have a writer, a penciller, an inker, a colorist, a letterer, a designer, editors, licensors, and all sorts of folks involved in the creation of the final comic.

"Seasons of Chaos" had a writer, **Ian Flynn**, who came up with the rough idea of the story that was presented to SEGA for initial approval. This process is called "pitching." The pitching process allows for creative conversations to happen early on, rather than writing the script and then having to make big changes. For example, at one point, "Seasons of Chaos" was going to be a silent story! Can you imagine reading it with no words and just the art?

When the pitch is approved, Ian begins writing the script. Like a movie script, a comic script describes the visual action of each page and the dialogue the characters say and think. Ian's scripts break the pages down into their individual panels and highlight important information like location, emotions, and other key details. Here are some script pages for "Seasons of Chaos."

PAGE ONE

PANEL 1 – Spring Valley Zone – Exterior – Day

Done in the style of a screen shot taken from a classic game.

SONIC, TAILS and AMY run through the "stage" from left to right. BADNIKS drift lazily in the background.

AMY is at left and springing off a very large flower reminiscent of a game spring.

SONIC comes out of a SPIN JUMP off of a BADNIK to give TAILS a surprised look. SONIC is at CENTER.

TAILS flies to the RIGHT and calls down to SONIC while pointing to something glinting in the distance.

1   TEXT BOX
    Spring Valley Zone.

PANEL 2 - The GREEN CHAOS EMERALD rests in the center of an especially large wildflower bloom.

SONIC takes center as he looks down at it in wonder. AMY and TAILS flank him and peer around him at the CHAOS EMERALD, gawking.

2   AMY
    Oh wow!
    A Chaos Emerald!

3   TAILS
    You don't normally see them lying around in the open!

PANEL 3 – SONIC smiles, self-satisfied, and reaches for the EMERALD.

4   SONIC
    I guess I'll just help myself.

PANEL 4 – Same staging as the previous panel. SONIC goes wide-eyed in a "Wait – what?" expression, hand still outstretched in mid-reach. A rush of BLUE whips past him as METAL SONIC takes the EMERALD at high speed.

PAGE FOUR

PANEL 1 – TAILS pivots in mid-air, straining to hurl SONIC higher. SONIC is flung from TAILS'S hands in a SPIN JUMP.

PANEL 2 – SONIC strains as he reaches for METAL SONIC'S foot. METAL SONIC looks back to see SONIC nearly grabbing him. Spring Valley Zone sprawls out beneath them.

PANEL 3 – METAL SONIC accelerates away, a compression wave marking the jolt of his thrust. SONIC is blown back by the thrust. (If you can render this after one of his falling sprite animations, that'd be a great visual gag)

1   SFX
    BWOOSH

2   SONIC
    YOW!

PANEL 4 – SONIC closes his eyes and reclines in the air as he free-falls. SONIC holds his hands above his head expectantly.

3   SONIC
    No worries. I'll just reach out and grab a perfectly timed
    air-support rescue from my bestest buddy in the whole world…

PANEL 5 – KNUCKLES glides towards us, hands held in front of him, catching SONIC. SONIC hangs from KNUCKLES'S fists and looks up at him, baffled. KNUCKLES frowns, serious.

4   SONIC
    --KNUCKLES?!

5   KNUCKLES
    Sonic.

6   SONIC
    What are you doing so far from home?

7   KNUCKLES
    There's trouble. You see…

Scripts often have to go through a few drafts before becoming final. The "Seasons of Chaos" script went through three rounds of revisions before final approval as the editorial team, a translator, and the team at SEGA reviewed the script and made notes to correct punctuation, spelling errors, and ideas to help make the story the best it can be! And while three rounds of revisions may sound like a lot, the notes on each round were pretty minor as Ian's a talented writer!

Once the script's approved, it moves to the art team! "Seasons of Chaos" was a group effort. While the majority of the pages were pencilled by **Aaron Hammerstrom**, both **Thomas Rothlisberger** and **Tracy Yardley** helped out too!

With the script in hand and plenty of reference material, Aaron roughed out all of the pages–loosely laying out the characters and action. From there, Aaron moved to pencilling the pages, taking those roughs and fleshing them out to be more clear and detailed. Check out some of Aaron's pencils and see how they match up with the script!

After Aaron finishes a page of pencils, they are handed over to one of the talented inkers on the story, **Reggie Graham** or **Matt Froese**. Reggie handled most of the front half of the story, while Matt tackled the back half. As inkers, their job is to refine Aaron's pencils further and prepare them for coloring.

Inkers help define the weight of the lines on the page, giving it additional depth, as well as filling in shadows and areas meant to be black. They also help round out some of the rougher edges of the penciled art. And they do it all while maintaining the original art as much as possible to keep the penciller's style! Look at how closely Reggie's inked pages resemble Aaron's pencils!

The next step of the process after inking is that the lineart (the combined pencil and inked pages) is sent to the colorist! Which in this case was a short journey since **Reggie Graham** was going on to colors directly from the lineart he finished (or received from the other inkers and line artists). Having pulled double duty on inks and colors, Reggie had a really clear vision of what the page would look like as it was finalized.

The coloring adds further depth to the world, using uniform colors on the characters to keep them consistent from page to page, while also creating special palettes for each seasonal zone in the story to make them visually distinct!

Once the art has been finalized and approved by SEGA and the editors, the book enters the production process. **Shawn Lee**, Art Director, Design & Production at IDW, puts all his skills to work. As a letterer, he puts all the dialogue and sound effects on the page (boy does he wish "Seasons of Chaos" had been a silent story)! Then as a designer, he assembles the lettered pages, all other material including covers, credits, design pages, and everything else, and makes it into the final product! His assembly even includes this "From Script to Page" behind-the-scenes feature!

With everything finally put together, the comic is reviewed once again by all the creators, editors **David Mariotte** and **Riley Farmer**, and the team at SEGA! When everyone's happy with it, the book is sent to print, sent to stores, and ends up here, in your hands!

IAN FLYNN INTERVIEW

*Continuing the celebration, we spoke with **Ian Flynn!** Besides writing "Seasons of Chaos," Ian is the most prolific Sonic writer, having worked on around 300 issues of Sonic comics, Sonic resource books, and much more since 2006. To celebrate Ian's 15th anniversary working on Sonic, we chatted with him about his time on the franchise!*

IDW *Hey Ian, thanks for chatting with us.*

IAN FLYNN My pleasure!

IDW *Let's start at the beginning, how did you first encounter Sonic?*

IF Long, long ago, in the before-times and the fabled age of 1992, my dad came home one day with the Sega Genesis/*Sonic the Hedgehog 2* combo. It was the first major console for our household, and my brother and I logged an unfathomable number of hours playing it. Two cartoons and a comic book series were coming out around that time, too, so Sonic was inescapable.

IDW *From there, how did you first get involved with Sonic comics?*

IF My best friend (whaddup Jeff!) was a big fan of the comics. In the 8th Grade, he gifted me a copy because he "felt like I should have it." Little did we know

he'd just set me on the course that would define the rest of my life.

IDW *What have been some of the highlights of your Sonic comic career?*

IF My longevity with the franchise is a big one. To work on something you've loved your whole life is a gift. To be involved for as long as I have, to have my work rendered by so many talented artists, to meet so many awesome fans and watch them grow up over the years–it's amazing. It's humbling. It makes me feel old–haha.

IDW *Because you've been such a prolific Sonic writer and have introduced so many characters and elements to the franchise, you're often seen as a Sonic expert. How's that affected your life outside of the comics?*

IF It got me a lot of excited calls and emails from friends and family when the movie was announced, and that was the *one* thing I didn't have a hand in! Folks also assume I have some kind of greater authority over the little blue hedgehog than I really do.

IDW *Speaking of Sonic outside of the comics, we hear you've got quite a collection of Sonic goodies amassed over the years. What are some favorite pieces of your collection?*

The crown jewel of the set so far are my Fang, Bean, and Bark plushes from the limited *Sonic the Fighters* series that were exclusive to Japan (I think?). I also have some amazing custom-made toys and models gifted to me by some incredibly talented and generous fans. I'm still missing a Blaze the Cat figure from the old Jazwares line, though (shakes fist).

Specifically to "Seasons of Chaos," much of your time writing Sonic has been his Modern interpretation. What are some of the differences you've experienced in writing Classic Sonic?

Classic Sonic is lighter in tone than Modern Sonic. The adventures are still grand, the perils still perilous, but it doesn't have quite the same dourness Modern Sonic stories sometimes have. Both are fun but in different ways.

One of the things that makes Sonic so appealing is his friends and foes. Who's your favorite character to write, besides Sonic, and who do you think you've most improved at writing over the years?

I get this question a lot and I hate it because I love them all! But Knuckles has always been one of my top favs since the beginning. And I relish any chance I get to write Bean. I'm very happy I got to carry over his characterization, along with Fang and Bark, from my previous work. As for "most improved," that might be Sonic. I think I've come to understand him a lot better over the years.

How has Sonic evolved as a character in the past 15 years that you've been chronicling his adventures?

He was created with the old '90s attitude, and that vision of "cool, irreverent rebel" died out with the decade. Who Sonic is has evolved with the trends, and I think he's begun to settle into a universal type of character that isn't so tied to the era he's currently living in.

How've you changed in the past 15 years of working on Sonic?

I've gotten heavier and hairier, but that's about it.

Are there any future Sonic projects that you can tease?

I do enjoy teasing everyone with my #KnowingSmile, but I have to play these close to the vest still. Rest assured I'm deeply involved with the Sonic series, and that's not changing any time soon.

Anything else you'd like to add?

A big shout-out to all my fellow fans-turned-pro who got to share in the dream. A big thank you to all the editors and collaborators I've worked with over the years–y'all make me look good. Even bigger thanks to my wife and fellow *Sonic* creator alumnus Aleah Baker who has vastly influenced my critical eye. And a heapin' helpin' of "thank you" to all the fans who have shared their love and support over the years. Y'all are a boundless well of creativity and energy, and I hope I can continue to entertain you all.

Thanks so much for talking with us, Ian, and giving us insight to your many years working on Sonic, and the many more years that you'll be sticking around!

Art by Tracy Yardley